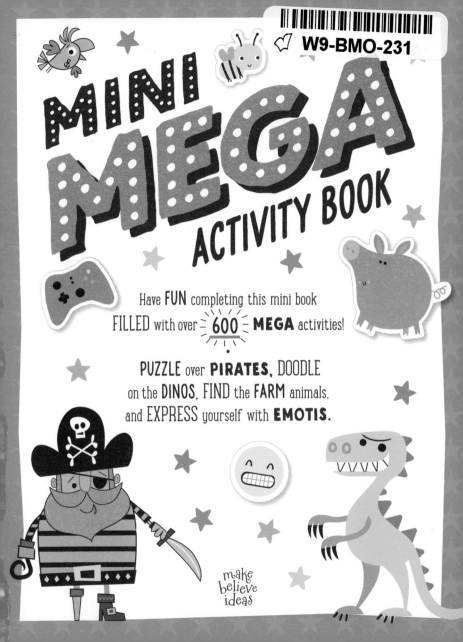

TREASURE HUNT

FIND and **CIRCLE** the ITEMS below:

1. **FIVE** GOLD COINS
2. **FOUR** EARRINGS
3. **THREE** SWORDS
4. **TWO** JEWELS
5. **SIX** PARROTS

6. **COLOR** the TREASURE CHEST.

2

CARNIVORE COLORING

7 **COLOR** this picture of **TAMMY** the **T. REX**.

8 **DRAW** some **SHARP TEETH!**

9 **DOODLE** some more **PLANTS.**

EGG SEARCH

DRAW a **LINE** from each DINOSAUR to its **MATCHING** colored **EGG**.

10

11

12

13

14 DOODLE some **SPOTS** on SAMMY the STEGOSAURUS.

EMOTI PATTERNS

Use **COLOR** to complete the **EMOTI** PATTERNS.

15

16

17

18

19

FARM FRIENDS

LOOK at the SCENE.
☑ the **BOXES** when you **FIND** the ANIMALS on the list.

20 **HOW MANY MICE** can you COUNT?

WRITE the ANSWER: _____

22	23	24	25	26
3 pigs	2 roosters	1 cow	2 horses	3 ducks

21 COLOR the TRACTOR.

27 5 chicks

28 4 sheep

29 2 turkeys

30 1 goat

31 1 fox

7

HOOK, LINE, AND SINKER

(32) Can you find SIX **DIFFERENCES** between the SCENES?

✓ the boxes when you **FIND** them.

| 1 | 2 | 3 | 4 | 5 | 6 |

DRAW THE LINE

33 DRAW a line from the START to FINISH. Visit all the EGGS, and don't go past any **VOLCANOES.**

Start →

34 **HOW MANY** VOLCANOES are there? WRITE the **ANSWER:** ....

Finish →

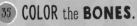

35 COLOR the **BONES.**

9

TASTY TREATS

CIRCLE the one that doesn't **MATCH** in each GROUP.

(36)

(37)
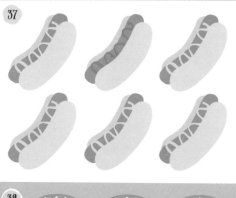

(38)

(39)
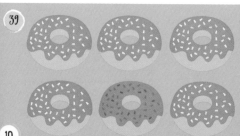

WORD FUN

40 COLOR the **ANIMALS**.

FIND the **WORDS** in the **WORD SEARCH**. **WORDS** can go **DOWN** or **ACROSS**.

a	r	b	n	o	s	w	h	l	p
s	n	r	t	q	r	x	o	z	w
o	b	a	r	n	t	r	r	a	e
k	r	n	a	y	r	b	s	n	u
a	i	e	c	l	w	o	e	u	p
s	y	o	t	l	k	d	f	h	i
h	j	m	o	s	u	t	d	j	g
e	a	u	r	t	r	a	u	n	s
e	i	p	i	z	b	a	c	w	y
p	s	h	c	h	i	c	k	c	l

41 barn

42 duck

43 chick

44 horse

45 pig

46 sheep

47 tractor

11

UP IN THE AIR

48 TRACE the CLOUDS.

49 CIRCLE three ORANGE **DRAGONFLIES**.

50 **GUIDE** the BUTTERFLY through the **MAZE** to reach its FRIENDS.

Start →

Finish ↓

12

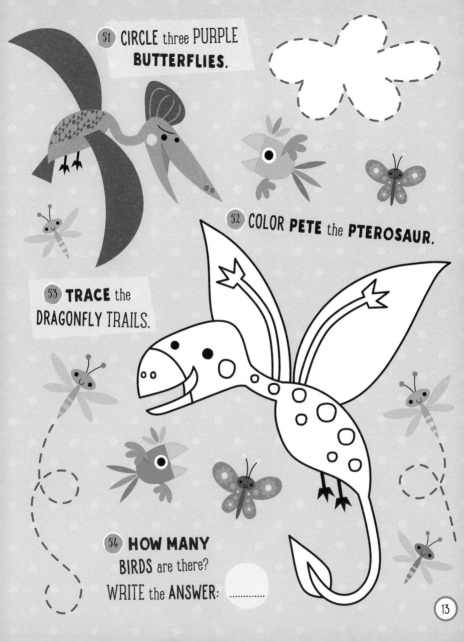

51 CIRCLE three PURPLE **BUTTERFLIES.**

52 COLOR **PETE** the **PTEROSAUR.**

53 **TRACE** the DRAGONFLY TRAILS.

54 **HOW MANY** BIRDS are there? WRITE the **ANSWER:** ....

QUICK QUIZ

CIRCLE the PICTURES to answer the QUESTIONS.

55 **WHO** doesn't **BELONG?**

56 **WHAT** holds **TREASURE?**

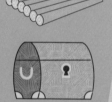

57 **WHICH** of these would you find on a **BOAT?**

58 **WHAT** doesn't **BELONG?**

59 **COLOR** the **SHELLS.**

COUNTING CLAWS

Help **SAM** the **STEGOSAURUS** finish the SUMS.

60 2 + 2 = ○

65 5 + 4 = ○

61 2 - 1 = ○

66 4 - 1 = ○

62 3 + 2 = ○

67 3 + 4 = ○

63 3 + 3 = ○

68 4 + 4 = ○

64 3 - 1 = ○

69 5 + 5 = ○

TRICKY TRACKS

70 COLOR the **TRACTORS** to MATCH their **TRAILERS**.

71 Which **TRACTOR** is TOWING the **PIGS?** WRITE the COLOR: ....

SAILOR SPELLING

TRACE the LETTERS to help the **CAPTAIN** spell out the **WORDS**.

72  parrot

73 turtle

74 gem

75 chest

76 **COLOR** the **TURTLE**.

17

SEARCH-O-SAURUS

FIND the **WORDS** in the **WORD SEARCH**. **WORDS** can go **DOWN OR ACROSS**.

h	q	w	e	h	r	c	t	o	p
s	p	i	k	e	s	a	a	c	x
p	x	s	x	v	o	r	e	x	e
i	h	o	p	r	i	n	x	w	x
f	o	o	t	p	r	i	n	t	t
s	r	x	c	x	a	v	o	r	i
c	n	s	l	v	p	o	k	e	n
a	q	l	a	t	t	r	x	r	c
l	x	p	w	b	o	e	l	a	t
e	r	l	s	a	r	x	s	r	x

77 carnivore

78 claws

79 extinct

80 footprint

81 horn

82 raptor

83 scale

84 spikes

85 **HOW MANY** BONES are there? WRITE the **ANSWER:** ....

18

PUTTING ON A SHOW

86 Can you **HELP** the **MUSICIAN** find his lost GUITAR?

Start

Finish

87 **COLOR** the audience **EMOTIS**.

FUN ON THE FARM

88 COPY the **HORSE**. Use the GRID to help you.

89 COPY the **COW**. Use the GRID to help you.

COLOR the LAMBS to **MATCH** their woolly **SWEATERS**.

21

WHAT'S IN A NAME?

Draw LINES to **MATCH UP** the dinosaur NAMES.

91 TRI

SAURUS

92 DIPLO

CERATOPS

93 STEGO

REX

94 T.

DOCUS

95 COLOR the DINOSAUR'S **SPOTS** BLUE.

22

COIN COUNT

Finish the **SUMS** to help the PIRATES count their COINS.

96 $1 + 4 = \ldots$

101 $5 - 3 = \ldots$

97 $4 - 1 = \ldots$

102 $8 + 2 = \ldots$

98 $5 + 1 = \ldots$

103 $3 + 5 = \ldots$

99 $2 + 5 = \ldots$

104 $6 - 5 = \ldots$

100 $5 - 1 = \ldots$

105 $5 + 4 = \ldots$

EMOTI-SHIRT

106

DRAW and DOODLE cool **EMOTI** designs on the T-SHIRTS.

107

108

DINO BUDDIES

Use the **CLUES** to find out which DINOSAUR
is **ABI** the **ANKYLOSAURUS'S** best **FRIEND**.

Sam the Stegosaurus

Dan the Diplodocus

Ann the Allosaurus

Sophie the Spinosaurus

Val the Velociraptor

Tom the T. rex

CLUE 1:
The dinosaur has
green spots.

CLUE 2:
The dinosaur has
orange spikes.

CLUE 3:
The dinosaur has
big teeth.

112 **CIRCLE ABI** the
ANKYLOSAURUS'S
FRIEND.

113 **HOW MANY**
EGGS are there?
WRITE the **ANSWER:** ....

114 **COLOR** the
dinosaur **FOOTPRINTS.**

LOTS OF DOTS

115 DRAW CLOUDS in the **SKY**.

116 JOIN the DOTS to SEE what's in the **FIELD**.

117 **HOW MANY** RABBITS are there? WRITE the **ANSWER**:

PIRATE PARTY

The **PIRATES** are having a PARTY.
118 COLOR the **BALLOONS**.

119 FIND and **CIRCLE** the JEWEL that looks **EXACTLY** like THIS one.

120 **HOW MANY** CUPCAKES are there? WRITE the **ANSWER**: ....

121 **COLOR** the PIRATE.

122 DOODLE a DESIGN on the **HAT**.

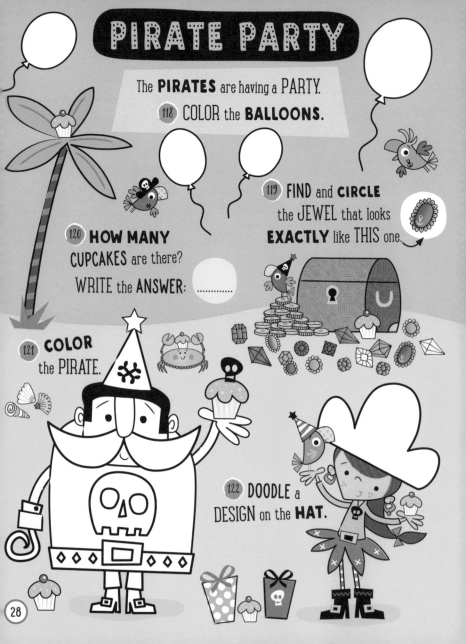

123 DRAW a MUSTACHE on the **PIRATE**.

124 DRAW an EYEPATCH on the **PIRATE**.

125 CIRCLE the **ONE THAT'S DIFFERENT** in each **ROW**.

126 COMPLETE the PIRATE **SUMS**.

$$4 + 1 = \text{......}$$

$$6 - 3 = \text{......}$$

$$7 + 2 = \text{......}$$

29

DINO FRIENDS

127 Can you find **SIX DIFFERENCES** between the SCENES?

✓ the **BOXES** when you **FIND** them.

| 1 | 2 | 3 | 4 | 5 | 6 |

CRAZY CREATURES

DRAW funny FACES on the **ANIMALS**.

PICTURE PUZZLER

132 FIND and CIRCLE three **PURPLE** creatures.

WRITE the missing **LETTERS** to finish the WORDS.

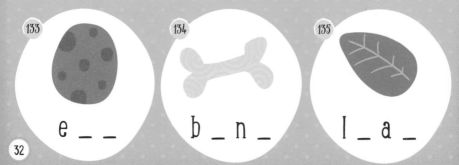

133 e _ _

134 b _ n _

135 l _ a _

NAME GAME

136

DRAW a LINE to CONNECT the PIRATES to their NAMES.

137

Parrot Percy

138

Sailor Susan

Captain Claude

139

140 **COLOR** the PARROT.

First Mate Mike

PREHISTORIC PATTERNS

Use **COLOR** to complete the **PREHISTORIC** PATTERNS.

WONDERFUL WORDS

FIND the **WORDS** in the WORD SEARCH.
WORDS can go DOWN or **ACROSS**.

✓ each WORD when you've **FOUND** it.

a	s	n	a	p	p	l	r	s	a
p	t	t	r	s	h	e	e	p	s
p	r	f	a	r	l	a	m	f	r
l	a	z	c	h	i	c	k	e	n
e	w	n	o	y	r	c	l	f	a
b	b	c	w	o	r	z	l	a	n
c	e	t	r	y	m	b	n	r	f
b	r	c	o	k	l	a	u	m	s
g	r	p	d	u	c	k	b	e	r
k	y	t	r	a	i	l	e	r	m

145
apple

146
chicken

147
cow

148
duck

149
farmer

150
sheep

151
strawberry

152
trailer

35

SILLY SCRAMBLE

UNSCRAMBLE the **WORDS** below.
USE the **PICTURES** to **GUIDE** you.
Then **WRITE** the words on the **DOTTED LINES**.

EVCA

153 ....

DIRB

154 ....

ACONVOL

155 ....

ORWELF

156 ....

157 **HOW MANY**
DRAGONFLIES are there?
WRITE the **ANSWER:** ....

36

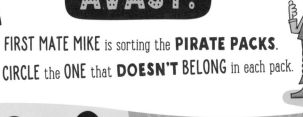

FIRST MATE MIKE is sorting the **PIRATE PACKS**.
CIRCLE the ONE that **DOESN'T** BELONG in each pack.

158

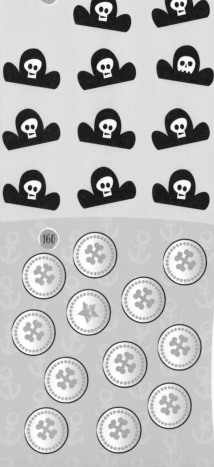

159

160

161

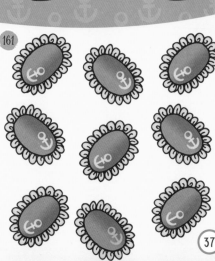

TERRIFIC TRACTOR

LABEL the **PICTURE** using the **WORDS** listed below:

162 tree   163 tire   164 sun   165 wheel

166 pig   167 light   168 trailer   169 farmer

f _ _ _ _ _ r

s _ _

t _ _ _

l i _ _ _ _

p _ _

tr _ _ l _ _   t _ _ _   w _ _ _ l

170 Now **COLOR** the **TRACTOR**.

EMOTI FUN

DESIGN your own **EMOTIS** for the things you think are really FUN.
Then write the **NAME** of the thing in the space beneath each FRAME.

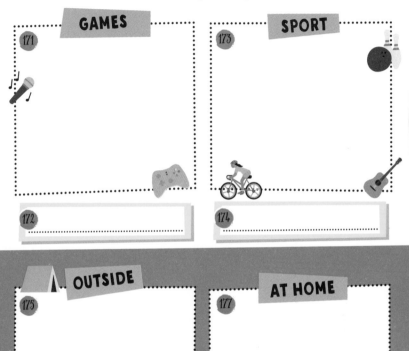

GAMES

171

SPORT

173

172

174

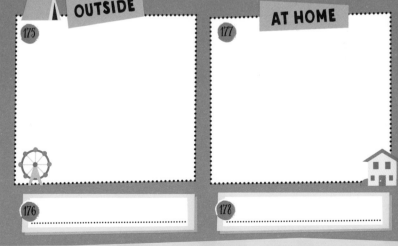

OUTSIDE

175

AT HOME

177

176

178

DIPLODOCUS MATH

Help **DAN** the **DIPLODOCUS** finish the **SUMS**.

179
9 - 8 = ...

184
6 + 1 = ...

180
4 + ... = 10

185
6 + ... = 8

181
.... + 4 = 5

186
.... - 3 = 2

182
2 + ... = 6

187
2 + ... = 4

183
7 - 4 = ...

188
6 + 3 = ...

RIGGING RACE

189 Draw a **LINE** from START to **FINISH**.
Collect all of the **JEWELS** on the way.
and **AVOID** the pesky PARROTS!

Finish

Start

190 **HOW MANY**
JEWELS did you collect?
WRITE the **ANSWER:** ....

191 **COLOR**
the PARROTS.

41

HAPPY HARVEST

Use **COLOR** to complete the **HARVEST** PATTERNS.

192

193

194

195

X MARKS THE SPOT

196 **FOLLOW** the **LINES** to see who **REACHES** the **TREASURE**.

197 COLOR the TREASURE.

LABEL ME!

LABEL the **CREATURES** using the WORDS listed below:

198 claw	199 leg	200 scales	201 spike	202 teeth
203 horn	204 spots	205 snout	206 tail	207 fin

f _ _

s _ _ _ t

s _ i _ _

s _ _ l _ _

t _ _ _

t _ _ _ h

c _ _ w

h _ _ _

s p _ _ _

l _ _

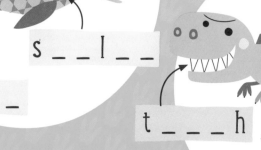

44

RUSH HOUR

WRITE the ANSWERS to the QUESTIONS below.

 208 HOW MANY BUSES are there?

....

 209 HOW MANY YELLOW CARS are there?

....

 210 HOW MANY TRAIN CARS are there?

....

45

BACK ON TRACK

Draw **LINES** to match the
ANIMALS to their FOOTPRINTS.

211

212

213

214

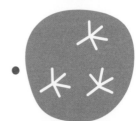

COLOR BY NUMBERS

215 Use the **KEY** below to **COLOR** the PICTURE.

SAVVY SPELLER

TRACE the **LETTERS** to help
SAILOR SERENA spell out the **WORDS**.

216 hat

217 coins

218 ship

219 flag

220 COLOR the **FLAG**.

48

BY THE BARN

221 Can you find FIVE **DIFFERENCES** between the SCENES?

✓ the **BOXES** when you **FIND** them.

| 1 | 2 | 3 | 4 | 5 | 6 |

49

TIME FOR TEA

The **DINOSAURS** are HUNGRY.

222 FIND and CIRCLE **FIVE** pieces of FOOD.

223 Doodle **PATTERNS** on the **EGGS**, and then COLOR them in.

PIRATE COPY AND COLOR

224 Use the **GRIDS** to FINISH the ITEMS **BELOW**.

JOLLY ROGER

225 Now **COLOR** it!

SWORD

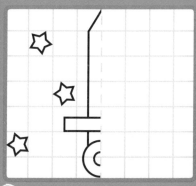

226 DOODLE some GEMS on the **HILT**.

TREASURE CHEST

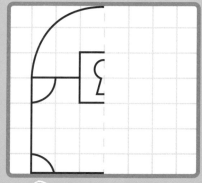

227 **DRAW** some COINS around the **CHEST**.

PIRATE

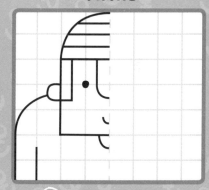

228 **DOODLE** a funny MUSTACHE and **BEARD**.

HEDGE MAZE

229 Follow the **TRAILS** to see who reaches the **MIDDLE** of the HEDGE MAZE.

Start

Start

turkey

goat

Finish

dog

Start

230 COLOR the **DOG**.

Write the **ANIMAL** that reached the MIDDLE of the MAZE.

231 ....

FLORA'S FOOD

232 COLOR the **FOOD** on the SHELVES.

Look at the **SHELVES**. ✔ the BOXES when you **FIND** the things on the **LIST**.

233 3 apples

234 2 loaves of bread

235 4 carrots

236 1 piece of cheese

53

WHO'S WHO?

Look at the **PICTURES** BELOW.
WRITE the **NAMES** to **ANSWER** the QUESTIONS.

Who has **BLUE** SPOTS?

237 E ....

Who has **RED** WINGS?

238 C ....

Who has a **PURPLE** TAIL?

239 C ....

Who has **WHITE** TEETH?

240 R ....

Bob

Charlie

Rose

Mary

Ellie

Chris

Connie

Ryan

JOKING AROUND

Draw **LINES** to match the **ANSWERS** to the JOKES.

241 Why couldn't the PIRATE learn the **ALPHABET?**

It was on **SAIL!**

242 What SHIVERS at the bottom of the OCEAN?

He spent too **LONG** at **C!**

243 Why was the PIRATE SHIP so **CHEAP?**

Because they **ARRRRRRE!**

244 Why are **PIRATES** called PIRATES?

A NERVOUS **WRECK!**

55

FLOWER FUN

CIRCLE the **FLOWER** that doesn't BELONG in each ROW.

245

246

247

248 COLOR the **FLOWERS**.

249 DECORATE the **PETALS** with PRETTY PATTERNS.

DINO DISORDER

UNSCRAMBLE the WORDS below.
USE the **PICTURES** to **GUIDE** you.
Then **WRITE** the words on the DOTTED LINES.

NOEB

250 ....

HNSOR

251 ....

ETETH

252 ....

LAIT

253 ....

254 **HOW MANY**
FOOTPRINTS are there?
WRITE the **ANSWER:** ....

WORD SEARCH

255 COLOR the **PICTURES**.

Search the **GRID** for the **PIRATE** words below. **WORDS** can go DOWN or **ACROSS**.

✔ each WORD when you've **FOUND** IT.

a	c	d	s	w	o	r	d	f	p
f	g	s	t	i	j	c	l	t	i
l	u	v	l	w	m	a	p	t	r
a	r	a	y	z	r	i	a	p	a
g	t	r	e	a	s	u	r	e	t
v	y	i	x	r	a	o	c	m	e
t	s	h	i	p	y	q	k	t	y
u	i	j	k	f	e	y	t	n	d
p	a	r	o	l	z	v	w	u	b
h	y	m	e	r	m	a	i	d	o

256
flag

257
map

258
mermaid

259
pirate

260
ship

261
sword

262
treasure

58

PERFECT PORTRAITS

263 TRACE the **FARMER**.

264 DOODLE some **FLOWERS**.

265 COLOR the CORN.

266 DRAW **CARROTS** for the RABBIT.

267 DESIGN a **PATTERN** on the EGG.

UNDER THE SEA

268 DRAW some WIGGLY LEGS for the **JELLYFISH!**

269 CONNECT the **DOTS** to finish the **PICTURE.**

270 Now **COLOR** it in.

271 **HOW MANY** FISH are there? WRITE the **ANSWER**: ....

272 DRAW **RAINDROPS** in the SKY.

273 DOODLE some beautiful FLOWERS.

274 **DECORATE** the **UMBRELLAS** with swirly PATTERNS.

275 COLOR the DUCKS' **BOOTS**.

276 DESIGN **EMOTI SIGNS** to put in your DEN.

KEEP OUT!

SHHH!

SECRET MEETING

COME IN

277 COLOR the **FUN** ACTIVITIES.

278 Now CIRCLE your **FAVORITE.**

279 DOODLE **EMOTIS** on the BACKPACK

280 COLOR the tasty **SNACKS**.

281 Now **CIRCLE** your top three SNACKS.

FOREST FUN

282 Finish **COLORING** the scene.

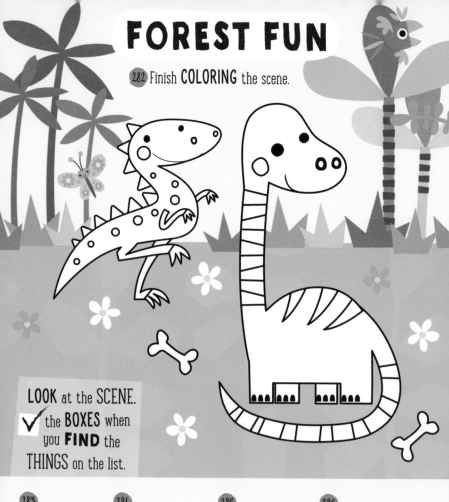

LOOK at the **SCENE.**
✓ the **BOXES** when
you **FIND** the
THINGS on the list.

283

1 T. rex

284

2 birds

285

3 eggs

286

1 pink butterfly

287

3 bones

288
4 purple flowers

289

1 dragonfly

290

2 velociraptor

KEEP FIT

291 Can you **HELP** the **ATHLETE** find her TENNIS RACKET?

Start

Finish

292 **COLOR** the sporty **EMOTIS.**

BIRDS OF A FEATHER

293

FIND and CIRCLE the **PARROTS** that look EXACTLY like these.

294

295 COPY the **ANCHOR.** Use the GRID to help you.

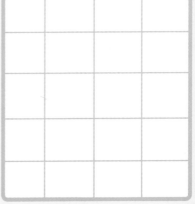

FIND THE DIFFERENCE

Can you find **FIVE DIFFERENCES** between the SCENES?

✔ the **BOXES** when you **FIND** them.

1 2 3 4 5

JURASSIC JUMBLE

UNSCRAMBLE the WORDS below.
USE the PICTURES to **GUIDE** you.
Then **WRITE** the words on the DOTTED LINES.

 297 D N S A U R I O
....

 298 W L C A
....

299 B N E O
....

300 E L A F
....

 301 E V C A
....

302 G E G
....

 303 W N G I
....

 304 V L O A C O N
....

 305 **FIND** the WORDS in the WORD SEARCH. WORDS can go DOWN or **ACROSS.**

b	o	c	a	v	e	l	o
c	a	l	z	e	g	g	i
d	l	e	a	f	n	o	v
i	d	i	n	s	r	a	o
n	w	l	j	c	a	w	l
o	i	v	o	l	y	n	c
s	n	a	e	a	i	o	a
a	g	u	w	w	i	n	n
u	d	r	n	c	l	a	o
r	m	w	b	o	n	e	i

69

MORNING ALARM

306 COLOR the **ROOSTER**.

307 COLOR the ALARM CLOCK.

308 DRAW the HANDS on to show **SEVEN** o'clock.

309 **HOW MANY** CHICKS are there? WRITE the **ANSWER:** ....

PLENTY OF FISH

310 Follow the **LINES** to see which **PIRATE** has caught the FISH.

311 COLOR the RAFT.

312 **HOW MANY** PARROTS are there? WRITE the **ANSWER:**

71

DISCOVERY DINO

FIND and CIRCLE the missing FIVE DINOS:

313 314 315 316 317

318 **HOW MANY**

PURPLE BONES are there?
WRITE the **ANSWER:** ....

TREASURE ISLAND

The **PIRATES** have found an **ISLAND** of TREASURE!

319 COLOR the PIRATE'S HAT.

320 COLOR the GIANT JEWEL.

321 TRACE the **TRAILS** and FIND the **CRAB'S** JEWELS.

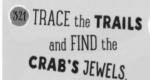

322 CIRCLE the **MERMAID** NECKLACE.

323 **HOW MANY** BLUE JEWELS can you **COUNT?**

324 **COLOR** the **PIRATE.** Use the **COLORED DOTS** to **GUIDE** you.

325 **COLOR** the **BARREL** of **JEWELS.**

75

PARTY TIME

HELP **FARMER** FRED prepare for a **PARTY**.

326 TRACE party **HATS** on the SHEEP.

327 Use **COLOR** to FINISH the CAKE.

328 HOW MANY CANDLES are there? WRITE THE ANSWER: ....

CONNECT AND COPY

DRAW A LINE from each BONE to the MATCHING colored DINOSAUR.

329 330 331

332 COPY the PICTURE.
Use the GRID to HELP you.

Then COLOR it in!

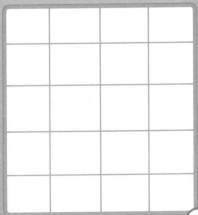

ANIMAL ROWS

CIRCLE the ONE that DOESN'T belong in each ROW.

333

334

335

336

337

SILLY SCENE

338 This **SCENE** isn't quite **RIGHT!**
FIND **SIX** THINGS that **DON'T BELONG.**

✓ the **BOXES** when you **FIND** them.

PIRATE PUZZLE

UNSCRAMBLE the WORDS below.
USE the **PICTURES** as a GUIDE.

EJLWE

339 ....

ARPORT

340 ....

TAEIRP

341 ....

HTSEC

342 ....

343 **HOW MANY** SHELLS
can you **COUNT?**
WRITE the **ANSWER:** ....

CANNONBALL COUNT

Finish the **SUMS** to help the CAPTAIN count the **CANNONBALLS**.

344
$6 + \text{......} = 10$

349
$11 - 2 = \text{......}$

345
$2 + 4 = \text{......}$

350
$8 - \text{......} = 2$

346
$7 + \text{......} = 9$

351
$7 - 3 = \text{......}$

347
$4 + 4 = \text{......}$

352
$10 - \text{......} = 5$

348
$8 + \text{......} = 10$

353
$9 - 6 = \text{......}$

GOING DOTTY

354 **CONNECT** the DOTS to **FINISH** the PICTURE.

THEN COLOR it in!

355 **HOW MANY** FISH are there? WRITE the **ANSWER**: ....

356 **COPY** the COLORS of the BIG underwater **VOLCANO** to FINISH the SMALLER one.

82

MYSTERY EGG

357 **FOLLOW** the **LINES** to see **WHICH HEN** laid the **COLORFUL** EGG.

358 **HOW MANY** WHITE EGGS can you **SEE?**
WRITE the **ANSWER:** ....

359 **COLOR** the HENS to FINISH the **SCENE.**

ANCHORS AWAY!

360 FOLLOW the **ROPES** to see which BOAT has DROPPED its **ANCHOR**.

361 DOODLE a **PIRATE** DESIGN on the SAIL.

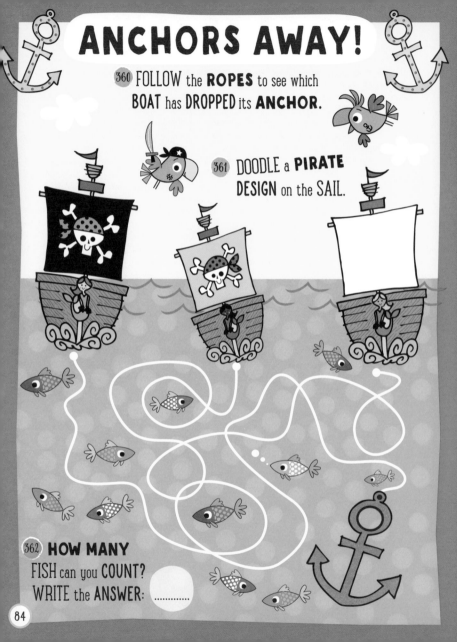

362 **HOW MANY** FISH can you COUNT? WRITE the ANSWER: ....

DINNER DASH

363 GUIDE BETTY the **BRACHIOSAURUS** through the **MAZE** to REACH her DINNER.

364 **COLOR** TERRY the PTERODACTYL.

Start

Finish

365 **HOW MANY** EGGS can you COUNT? WRITE the ANSWER: ....

85

BOTTOM OF THE SEA

366 COLOR the **SHIPWRECK**.

367 **HOW MANY** SEASHELLS can you COUNT? WRITE the **ANSWER:** ....

368 GUIDE the **FISH** through the MAZE to REACH his FRIENDS. **WATCH OUT** for the SEAWEED!

Start

Finish

369 **COLOR** the OCTOPUS.

370 Circle FIVE **YELLOW** fish.

371 **JOIN** the **DOTS** to REVEAL who's **LURKING** in the DEEP.

372 Then **COLOR** it in.

BUSY FARM

WRITE the **ANSWERS** to the QUESTIONS below.

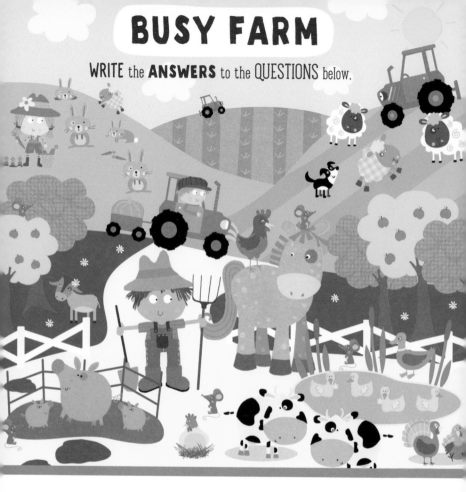

373 HOW MANY TRACTORS can you **COUNT?**

375 HOW MANY MICE can you **COUNT?**

374 HOW MANY SHEEP can you **COUNT?**

376 HOW MANY DUCKLINGS can you **COUNT?**

TRACE AND SEE

377 **COLOR** the FLOWERS.

378 **TRACE** the LINES to see WHO'S in the CAVE.

379 Then **DRAW** a FACE.

380 Now add COLOR!

MY FRIENDS

In the FRAMES, **DRAW** your FRIENDS as **EMOTIS**.
Then WRITE their **NAME** underneath!

CAPTAIN'S KITCHEN

389 COLOR CAPTAIN CALLUM'S KITCHEN.

390 DECORATE the **CUPCAKES** with YUMMY TOPPINGS.

FIND the THING that DOESN'T BELONG on EACH SHELF.

391

STARRRRVING · YO, HO, DOUGH! · STARTERS OF THE SEVEN SEAS · CAPTAIN'S COOKBOOK · STEWS FOR CREWS · BAKING FOR PIRATES

392

P · S

393

394 DOODLE a YUMMY plate of FOOD for the PIRATES.

395 THEN COLOR it in.

396 HOW MANY VEGETABLES can you COUNT? WRITE the ANSWER: ....

EMOTI PAIRS

DRAW LINES to MATCH the PAIRS.

 397   398   399   400   401   402

94

TRACE AND SEE

FIND the **MISSING LETTERS** to help **ADAM** the **ALLOSAURUS SPELL** out the **WORDS**.

403 COLOR ADAM the **ALLOSAURUS**.

404 c l __ w

405 b __ n e s

406 t a __ l

407 __ e e t h

408 COLOR the **BONES**.

409 FIND and **CIRCLE FIVE DRAGONFLIES**.

410 HOW MANY BONES are there? WRITE the **ANSWER**: ....

95

WHIRRING WINDMILL

It's **SPRING TIME** in the **WINDMILL** FIELD.

411 COLOR the **WINDMILL**.

412 **HOW MANY** SHEEP can you COUNT? WRITE the **ANSWER**:

....

413 DRAW more SEEDS to **FEED** the CHICKS.

414 CIRCLE SEVEN **FLOWERS**.

415 DRAW more **APPLES** on the TREES.

416 **DECORATE** the TRACTOR.

417 **DRAW** a DRIVER.

CARLA'S COLLECTION

FINISH the SUMS to HELP
CAPTAIN CARLA count the JEWELS.

418. $9 + \text{\_\_\_\_} = 11$

419. $4 + 9 = \text{\_\_\_\_}$

420. $12 - \text{\_\_\_\_} = 6$

421. $\text{\_\_\_\_} + 7 = 14$

VOLCANO VIEW

422 COLOR the SCENE to FINISH the **VOLCANO** VIEW.

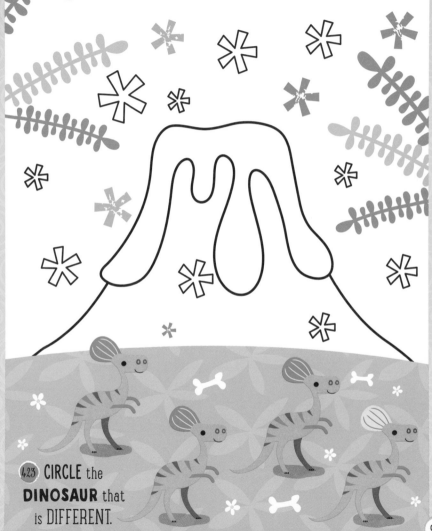

423 CIRCLE the **DINOSAUR** that is DIFFERENT.

99

SUPER STAMPS

Use **COLOR** and DOODLES to **CREATE** your own **STAMPS**.
YOU could **DRAW** your **FRIENDS**, **ANIMALS**, or **FAVORITE** PLACES.

424

425

426

427

428

429

DINO ART

430 **CONNECT** the **NUMBERED DOTS** to **COMPLETE** the **PICTURE**. Then **COLOR** it in!

431 **COLOR** the LAVA.

432 **FIND** and **CIRCLE** the ANT.

WHICH WAY?

HELP the **PIRATE CAPTAIN** get to his HAT!

433 Use the **KEY** to DRAW a LINE from **START** to FINISH. **DO NOT** go THROUGH the SKULL and **CROSSBONES**.

KEY:

Start

434 COLOR the PARROT.

Finish

435 DOODLE a DESIGN on the **HAT**.

102

TREASURE SEEKERS

Who has **FOUND** the **MOST JEWELS?**
COUNT the **JEWELS** for each **FRIEND,** and **WRITE** the **TOTAL** BELOW.

436

437

438

439 CIRCLE SEVEN **GOLD COINS.**

103

T.REX TROUBLE

LOOK at the **PICTURES**. WRITE the LETTER to answer the QUESTIONS below.

440 Who has **PURPLE SPIKES?**

....

441 Who has a **CURLY TAIL?**

....

442 Who has **THREE HORNS?**

....

ANIMAL FUN

443 **COPY** the **CHICKEN**. Use the **GRID** to **HELP** you.

444 **DOODLE** some **APPLES** on the **TREE**.

445 **COLOR** the **FLOWERS**.

PICTURE PERFECT

446 TRACE the **LETTERS** to reveal what the **PARROT** is SAYING.

polly

447 HOW many **PALM TREES** can you COUNT?
WRITE the ANSWER: ....

448 Use the **KEY** below to **COLOR** the **PICTURE**.

| 1 | 2 | 3 | 4 | 5 | 6 | 7 | 8 |

FUNNY FACES

DOODLE EMOTI FACES in the **YELLOW** CIRCLES.

449

450

451

452

453

454

455

456

DINO DOODLES

457 Copy **TINA** the **TRICERATOPS**. Use the **GRID** to **GUIDE** you.

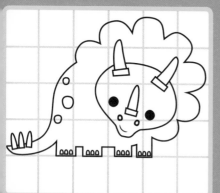

458 Use the **GRID** to finish the **DINO FOOTPRINT**.

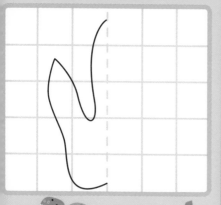

459 Use the **GRID** to finish the **DINO EGG**.

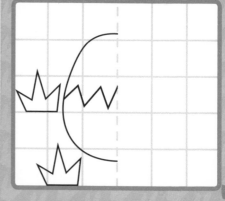

PRIZE PUMPKINS

The **FARMERS** are competing to GROW the **BIGGEST** PUMPKINS.
460 **CIRCLE** the BIGGEST one.

461 **DRAW FACES** on the **PUMPKINS.**

462 **COLOR** the TROPHY.

WHO'S WHO?

Look at the **PICTURES** BELOW.
WRITE the NAMES to **ANSWER** the QUESTIONS.

Who has a **PINK** BANDANA?

463 **C** _____

Who has **ONE** GOLD EARRING?

464 **G** _____

Who has a **PARROT?**

465 **J** _____

Who is wearing **PURPLE** PANTS?

466 **S** _____

Who has a **HEART** TATTOO?

467 **R** _____

Who is PLAYING the **ACCORDION?**

468 **S** _____

Rodney

Claude

Padma

Steve

Jenny

Claire

Gregory

Susan

MOLTEN MATHS

HELP **TOM** the **T. REX** finish the SUMS.

469) .... + 2 = 8

470) 7 + 4 = ...

471) 13 - 3 = ...

472) 10 + ... = 15

MY EMOTI DESIGNS

DESIGN new **EMOTIS** for these DIFFERENT things:

473

CAMPING

474 **DINOSAUR**

475

HOMEWORK

476 **COOKING**

477 CASTLE

478

SCHOOL

479

SURFING

480 A SELFIE

MOMMY MIX-UP

DRAW lines to MATCH the **BABY ANIMALS** to their MOMS.

481

482

483

484

PARROT PANIC

FIND all the WORDS in the WORD SEARCH.
WORDS can go DOWN or ACROSS.

 485 anchor

 486 cannon

 487 flag

 488 island

 489 jewel

490 parrot

491 rigging

492 ship

493 skull

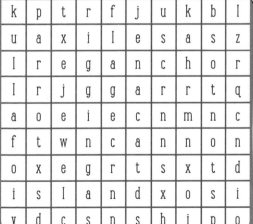

s	h	q	f	y	a	s	d	u	q
k	p	t	r	f	j	u	k	b	l
u	a	x	i	l	e	s	a	s	z
l	r	e	g	a	n	c	h	o	r
l	r	j	g	g	a	r	r	t	q
a	o	e	i	e	c	n	m	n	c
f	t	w	n	c	a	n	n	o	n
o	x	e	g	r	t	s	x	t	d
i	s	l	a	n	d	x	o	s	i
v	d	c	s	n	s	h	i	p	o

494 COLOR the PARROTS.

HOIST THE COLORS!

495 COLOR the PIRATE SHIP.

496 DECORATE the FLAGS.

497 DRAW a PIRATE in the PORTHOLE.

DINO DESIGNS

USE your COLORS to COMPLETE the DESIGNS.

498

499

500
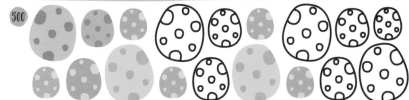

501

502

117

AHOY, ME HEARTIES!

503 **DOODLE** a cool **DESIGN** on the **BANDANA**.

504 **COLOR** the PIRATES.

505 Give them **NAMES:**

....

506 HOW many **BUCKETS** can you **SEE?** **WRITE** the **ANSWER:** ....

HUNGRY PIGS

507 GUIDE the **PIG** through the MAZE to reach his DINNER.

508 TRACE a CURLY TAIL for **PERCY** the **PIG**!

Start

Finish

509 COLOR the YUMMY **APPLES**.

SUPER STARS

510 TRACE the DOTS to create **PATTERNS** in the NIGHT SKY.

511 Use COLOR to **COMPLETE** the SCENE.

512 DRAW another **SNAIL**.

513 **CIRCLE** the FLOWER that DOESN'T match.

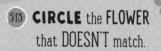

FAVORITE FLORA

DRAW a LINE from each **PTEROSAUR** to the matching **COLORED** FLOWER.

514

515

516

517

WORDS AHOY!

UNSCRAMBLE the **WORDS** below.
USE the **PICTURES** as a **GUIDE**.

SRODW

518 ....

THA

519 ....

AMP

520 ....

OINCS

521 ....

522 **HOW MANY** RED RUBIES
can you **COUNT**?
WRITE the **ANSWER:** ....

ODD ONE OUT

CIRCLE the one that **DOESN'T** belong in each **GROUP**.

(523)

(524)

(525)

(526)

PARROT GRUB

Look at the **PICTURES** BELOW.
WRITE the **NAMES** to **ANSWER** the QUESTIONS.

Who has a **GREEN** BEAK?

527 **P** ....

Who has **ORANGE** WINGS?

528 **H** ....

Who has an **ANCHOR** TATTOO?

529 **M** ....

Who is wearing a
BLUE BANDANA?

530 **F** ....

Who has a **YELLOW** tail?

531 **D** ....

Pia

Fiona

Harry

Dave

Clive

Percy

Darcy

Mike

532 **COLOR** the **CUPCAKES**.

124

SKY SCENE

533 CONNECT the **DOTS** to reveal the PICTURE.

534 THEN **COLOR** it in!

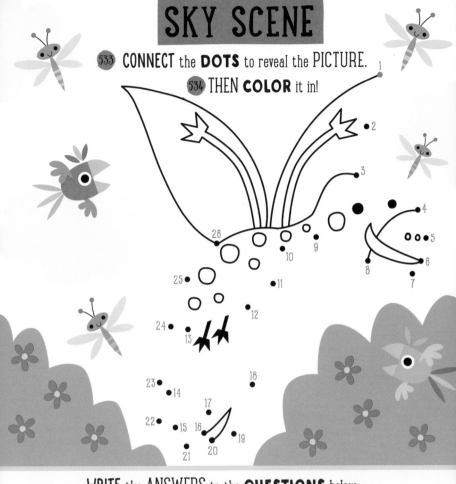

WRITE the ANSWERS to the **QUESTIONS** below:

535 How many **DRAGONFLIES** can you **COUNT?**

537 How many **FLOWERS** can you **COUNT?**

536 How many **BIRDS** can you **COUNT?**

538 How many **CLOUDS** can you **COUNT?**

SHARK ALERT

539 COLOR the **PIRATE** ship.

Start

540 **GUIDE** the PIRATE SHIP through the MAZE to reach the **TREASURE**. **WATCH OUT** for SHARKS!

Finish

541 COLOR the **SHELLS**.

HIDE·AND·SEEK

FIND and CIRCLE the **DINOSAURS** that look EXACTLY like THESE four:

542   543   544   545

FARMYARD FRIENDS

COPY the **PICTURES**. Use the **GRIDS** to **HELP** you.

546

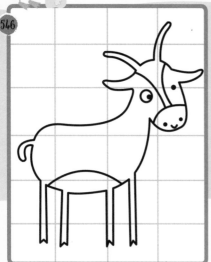

547

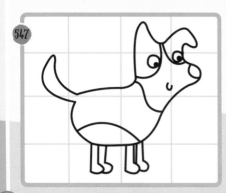

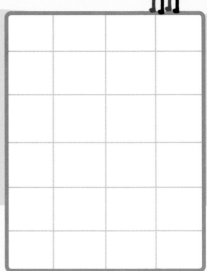

548

549

550 NOW COLOR them in!

DESERT ISLAND

Find all **EIGHT EMOTIS WORDS** in the **GRID**.
WORDS can go **DOWN** or **ACROSS**.

551 camera

552 fish

553 flamingo

554 flip-flops

555 magazine

x	s	k	y	g	a	w	f	p	f
g	o	p	m	h	s	a	l	o	l
b	p	l	a	n	e	t	i	l	a
x	a	p	g	x	b	e	p	e	m
m	x	d	a	s	a	r	f	m	i
a	w	t	z	t	y	m	l	v	n
g	a	f	i	s	h	e	o	q	g
a	f	q	n	x	t	l	p	e	o
t	r	e	e	q	w	o	s	o	p
c	a	m	e	r	a	n	e	r	a

556 plane   **557** tree   **558** watermelon

559 DRAW EMOTIS of the THREE **THINGS** you'd TAKE to a **DESERT ISLAND!**

130

WHICH WORD?

DRAW lines to FINISH each **PIRATE** phrase.

560 X MARKS THE... • • **PLANK!**

561 WALK THE... • • **TIMBERS!**

562 SHIVER ME... • • **SPOT!**

563 COLOR the JEWELS.

SUPER SCENE

564 Can you find **SIX DIFFERENCES** between the SCENES?

✓ the **BOXES** when you **FIND** them.

1	2	3	4	5	6

SHIPWRECKED!

565 The **SHIPWRECKED PIRATES** are HUNGRY!
Find and circle SIX pieces of FOOD.

✓ the boxes when you **FIND** them.

1	2	3	4	5	6

566 **DOODLE** PATTERNS on the SHELLS.

STARGAZING

FINISH the SUMS to COUNT the STARS.

567

572

568 + =

573

569

574

570 + =

575

571 − =

576

577 CONNECT the **DOTS** to finish the **PIRATE.**

578 Now **COLOR** him in.

579 FIND and CIRCLE three **CRABS.**

135

FIERCE FRAMES

580 COLOR the PICTURES in the **FRAMES**.

581 DRAW funny **HATS** on the DINOSAURS.

582 COLOR **ORANGE** stripes on **DAVE** the **DIPLODOCUS**.

583 DRAW a COLORFUL **DINOSAUR EGG** in the FRAME.

STORMY NIGHT

✓ **LOOK** at the **SCENE.**
✓ the **BOXES** when you
FIND the **ITEMS** on the list.

584
2 bottles ☐

585
2 sharks ☐

586
4 skulls ☐

587
1 parrot ☐

588
3 balloons ☐

589
3 pirates ☐

590
4 shells ☐

591
1 anchor ☐

592 **COLOR** the **RAINDROPS.**

FARMYARD ART

593 Use the **GRIDS** to FINISH the **PICTURES** below.

TRACTOR

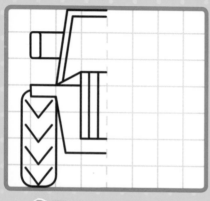

594 DRAW the **DRIVER**.

PIG

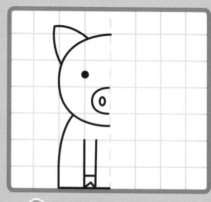

595 COLOR the pig **PINK**.

SCARECROW

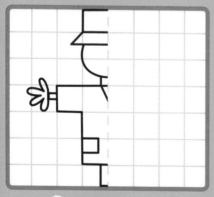

596 DRAW a silly **FACE**.

CAT

597 DRAW some curly **WHISKERS**.

DINO DRAWING

598. Use the clues below to DOODLE **DETAILS** on the DINOSAUR.

DRAW more **SPIKES**.

COLOR the DINO a BRIGHT color.

DRAW some **SPOTS**.

BURIED TREASURE

COUNT the JEWELS to see which **PIRATE** has the most BURIED TREASURE.

599 WRITE the **ANSWER:** ....

600 WRITE the **ANSWER:** ....

601 COLOR the **TROPHY.**